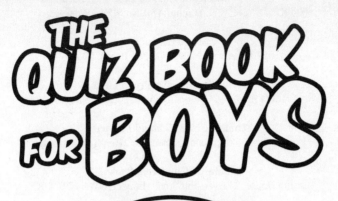

THE QUIZ BOOK FOR BOYS

by

H. Becker

Scholastic Canada Ltd.

Toronto New York London Auckland Sydney
Mexico City New Delhi Hong Kong Buenos Aires

Scholastic Canada Ltd.
604 King Street West, Toronto, Ontario M5V 1E1, Canada

Scholastic Inc.
557 Broadway, New York, NY 10012, USA

Scholastic Australia Pty Limited
PO Box 579, Gosford, NSW 2250, Australia

Scholastic New Zealand Limited
Private Bag 94407, Botany, Manukau 2163, New Zealand

Scholastic Children's Books
Euston House, 24 Eversholt Street, London NW1 1DB, UK

o ǐl

Illustrations copyright © shutterstock, with the following exceptions:
Pages 1, 4, 5 (middle), 10 (bottom), 35, 67 and 78 © copyright istock.com
Pages 21 (bottom), 29 (bottom), 30 (bottom), 56 and 77, © copyright dreamstime
Pages 44–45, courtesy of Simon Kwan © 2010 Scholastic Canada Ltd.,
page 17, courtesy of Sampar © 2010 Scholastic Canada Ltd.

ISBN 978-0-545-98032-6

6 5 4 3 2 1   Printed in Canada 121   10 11 12 13 14

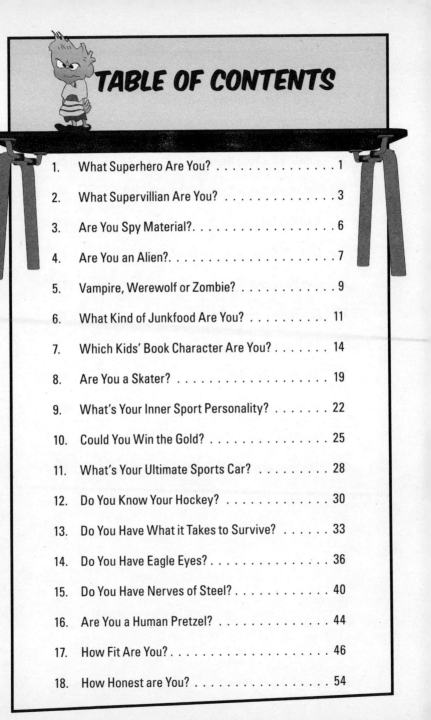

TABLE OF CONTENTS

WHAT SUPERHERO ARE YOU?

Answer yes or no to each of the following:

1. I like to fly.
2. I am super strong.
3. I like animals.
4. I consider myself to be kind of geeky and smart.
5. I have a secret dark side.
6. I am good at gymnastics.
7. I like hi-tech gadgets.
8. I have a bad temper.
9. I am very loyal to my friends.
10. I am a bit of a show-off.

SCORING

Give yourself the following points for each yes answer.

1. Yes 20	5. Yes 5	9. Yes 25
2. Yes 5	6. Yes 25	10. Yes 1
3. Yes 5	7. Yes 1	
4. Yes 20	8. Yes 5	

1

YOU ARE . . .

0–20 Iron Man. You kind of like to brag, but who can blame you? You have the coolest gadgets on the planet (at least when Batman is on vacation). Consider a career in business or metalwork.

21–40 Wolverine. You have a taste for junk food and rare meat, but don't forget your veggies! You tend to think you are indestructible. Okay, you sort of are, but don't let it go to your fuzzy little head!

41–60 Superman. No one really understands you. That's because you never share your feelings with others. You have really nice legs, especially when you wear fetching blue tights. Avoid meteorites and headwinds.

61–80 Batman. You had a troubled past, which has led to a very weird present. You are super athletic. You are especially good at climbing, roping and hanging upside down from your toes.

81+ Spider-Man. You are the one to call on in a sticky situation. You find your role as a mutant superhero a stretch and are troubled by your extremely hairy legs. Thank goodness you're in great shape, have amazing eye-hand coordination and a mild manner to go along with it all.

WHAT SUPERVILLAIN ARE YOU?

Answer yes or no to each of the following:

1. I like to invent things.
2. Other people call me conceited.
3. People sometimes call me "crazy."
4. I enjoy practical jokes and making other people laugh till they cry.
5. I crave riches.
6. I crave power.
7. I am scientifically minded.
8. I like creating and solving puzzles.

SCORING

Give yourself the following points for each yes answer.

1. Yes 1	5. Yes 3
2. Yes 1	6. Yes 1
3. Yes 10	7. Yes 1
4. Yes 6	8. Yes 6

3

YOU ARE . . .

0–1 Sorry, you're not a supervillain — just an everyday regular villain. Maybe someday you'll get lucky and run into some freaky gamma rays . . .

2–5 Magneto. You can control electromagnetic radiation, such as light, x-rays and toaster ovens. You think you are pretty hot stuff, but that's just the heat from the exploding toasters.

6–10 Lex Luthor. You are greedy greedy greedy. You'll stop at nothing to take over the world. If only you had just one teeny little superpower, you could stop worrying and be happy.

11–15 Justin Hammer. It really bugs you when people have better clothes and gadgets than you. Why can't you be the first kid on the block with the latest toy for once?

16–20 The Green Goblin. You are a walking advertisement for workplace safety. You are so full of chemicals, you look like a tree frog — a clinically insane tree frog. You enjoy making pots of money, flying in your own iffy contraptions and stalking Peter Parker.

21+ The Joker. You may be a wee bit crazy. Okay, a lot crazy. You love destroying things and wearing really freaky clown makeup. Wherever you go, people run screaming for the hills. That's exactly how you like it. Words of advice: lose the green hair — it's soooo 1980s.

5

ARE YOU SPY MATERIAL?

TOP SECRET

True or false?

1. I am good at following directions.
2. I am very observant.
3. I have an excellent memory.
4. I am top of my class in all subjects.
5. I have average looks.
6. I am not very popular. But I am not unpopular either.
7. I get along well with people.
8. I blend in with the crowd.
9. I have a taste for adventure.
10. I can stick to a task for a long time, even if it is boring.
11. I can think on my feet.
12. I like keeping secrets.
13. I have a good imagination.
14. I am physically fit.
15. I am a good listener.
16. I am very even-tempered.
17. I am orderly and precise.
18. I am very patient.
19. I am detail-oriented.
20. I am able to put aside my own needs for a higher purpose.

WHAT YOUR SCORE MEANS

Give yourself one point for each true answer.

0–10. You'd probably make a better professional wrestler.

11–14. You have what it takes to become a secret agent. Bone up on your skills by reading your sister's diary.

15–16. You've got serious spy potential. Begin practicing your GNIDOCED skills now.

17–19. Don't be surprised if you're recruited by CSIS within the next six weeks. Be ready. You are the one your country will turn to when the chips are down.

20. Bond. James Bond.

ARE YOU AN ALIEN?

1. Which would you rather do?
a. Play a video game with alien invaders.
b. Play soccer with my friends.
c. Stare longingly at the sky.

2. Your head . . .
a. is beautifully shaped.
b. is shaped sort of like a football and can receive radio transmissions.
c. is part of a matched set.

3. Your favourite show is . . .
a. *Futurama*.
b. *Family Guy*.
c. *CBC News*.

4. What's your favourite subject in school?
a. Phys. ed.
b. Astronomy
c. Science

5. What do you call your parents?
a. Earth Mother and Earth Father.
b. Mom and Dad.
c. What are these Earth objects you call parents?

6. If you could travel anywhere, where would you go?
a. Someplace quiet with a great view, like the Moon.
b. Someplace exciting, like Betelgeuse.
c. Disney World.

7. Your earliest memory is . . .
a. being abducted by small green men and taken to the mothership.
b. a long journey in a small, but warm and cozy, craft.
c. getting stepped on by the dog.

8. How many fingers do you have?
a. Six. I mean five.
b. Five.
c. Five on each hand, so 20 all together.

9. What's your favourite snack?
a. Sunflower seeds.
b. Cow juice and a morsel of highly sweetened, cocoa flavoured carbohydrates.
c. Radium ions.

10. You feel most comfortable around . . .
a. kids my age.
b. slugs.
c. Zorks.

7

SCORING

1. a3 b1 c5
2. a1 b4 c5
3. a2 b1 c3
4. a1 b3 c2
5. a3 b1 c5
6. a5 b4 c1
7. a3 b5 c1
8. a2 b1 c5
9. a1 b2 c5
10. a1 b2 c5

OUT OF THIS WORLD RESULTS

10–15 Humanoid. You may be weird, but your oddness is of the ordinary human variety. Beware of little green men offering you rides, giant scorpions and anyone asking if they can "phone home."

16–30 Possible human-alien cross. You may have been kidnapped right out of your crib, or perhaps you became host to an alien life form. Either way, you combine human traits with some quirks that may indicate extra-terrestrial origins. If you do extremely well in math, underwater breathing and can blow things up with lasers that shoot from your eyes, you may wish to contact your local UFO centre.

31+ Alien. We mean you no harm. Please return to your planet and leave us earthlings in peace!

VAMPIRE, WEREWOLF OR ZOMBIE?

1. When you see a slice of rare meat, you tend to . . .
a. drool.
b. swallow it in one chunk.
c. say, "vergel mbing crowblud bechhhhhh!"

2. Your favourite outfit is . . .
a. a fur coat.
b. black. Anything black.
c. your "birthday suit."

3. When you wake up in the morning, what do you say?
a. "AAAAAARGGHH!!! The light! The light! It burns!"
b. "Arf! The light! It burns!"
c. "Good morning, Mother dearest."

4. The household chore that you like least is . . .
a. polishing silver.
b. washing windows.
c. gardening.

5. What life form speaks to you?
a. Bats
b. Dogs
c. Bacteria

6. Your hands are . . .
a. blue and decaying.
b. pale and delicate.
c. covered with fur.

7. Your breath smells like . . .
a. puppy chow.
b. dirt and fungus.
c. a rare roast beef sandwich.

8. Where would you prefer to live?
a. A castle in the Carpathian Mountains.
b. The forests of the Rockies.
c. A bustling city with a large cemetery.

9. Which fictional character is someone you can relate to?
a. Frankenstein
b. Batman, the "Caped Crusader"
c. The Abominable Snowman

10. If you were not a supernatural being, which job would you prefer?
a. Magician
b. Animal trainer
c. Undertaker

SCORING

1. a1 b2 c3
2. a2 b1 c3
3. a1 b2 c3
4. a2 b1 c3
5. a1 b2 c3
6. a3 b1 c2
7. a2 b3 c1
8. a1 b2 c3
9. a3 b1 c2
10. a1 b2 c3

YOU ARE A . . .

10–15 Vampire. "Count" yourself one of Dracula's minions. Avoid bright light and anyone with the last name Van Helsing. Your best subject in school: biology. Future job: emergency room physician.

16–20 Werewolf. So that's why you feel so tired when there's a full moon — it's from running around at night on all fours, howling at the sky. Make sure to comb your knuckles regularly to avoid detection. Your best subject in school: astronomy. Future job: pro hockey player.

21–30 Zombie. You reek, man! Take a bath now and again to hide the distinct scent of decay. You don't really care what people think about you, because you're only after one thing — their brains! Your best subjects in school: sign language and standing for "O Canada." Future job: prime minister.

WHAT KIND OF JUNK FOOD ARE YOU?

1. What best describes you?
a. A sweetheart
b. A tough guy
c. An athlete
d. A smart guy

2. Which country appeals to you most?
a. South Africa
b. England
c. Venezuela
d. Egypt

3. What sport do you prefer?
a. Rugby
b. Hockey
c. Tennis
d. Basketball

4. You'd rather . . .
a. watch sports on TV.
b. play sports.
c. play a video game.
d. play cards.

5. What kind of books do you like?
a. Adventure stories
b. Graphic novels
c. Sports stories
d. I don't like to read.

6. Your best quality is your . . .
a. intelligence.
b. sense of humour.
c. personality.
d. determination.

7. What job would you most like to have when you grow up?
a. Sports broadcaster
b. Firefighter, paramedic or soldier
c. Doctor
d. Teacher

8. Which colour do you prefer?
a. Red
b. Orange
c. Blue
d. Green

9. How would you describe yourself?
a. Tidy
b. Kind of a slob
c. Messy, but clean
d. Total clean freak

10. Which animal do you prefer?
a. Cheetah
b. Pterodactyl
c. Dog
d. Butterfly

SCORING

1. a4 b3 c2 d1
2. a2 b3 c1 d4
3. a2 b3 c4 d1
4. a3 b2 c1 d4
5. a1 b4 c2 d3
6. a2 b1 c4 d3
7. a3 b2 c3 d4
8. a2 b3 c4 d1
9. a4 b1 c3 d2
10. a2 b3 c1 d4

YOU ARE . . .

10–13 Nachos. You like variety in your life and you are good at sharing with others. Wherever there's a party, you're right in the thick of it!

14–17 Chips and dip. Skip the fancy-shmancy stuff. You like life best when it's simple and relaxed. Free and easy — that's you.

18–20 A foot-long hot dog. You always go whole hog — you know there's no sense waiting around for life to happen. You have a tendency to put your foot in your mouth.

21–25 Onion rings. Your favourite number is one. Your favourite cookies are Oreos. Your favourite animals are orangutans. You enjoy round robin tennis and circle dancing.

26–29 Chocolate chip cookies. You like to take life slowly, one bite at a time. You know how to pace yourself. Life is full of obstacles, but you can rise above them to see the big picture.

30–32 A slushie. You prefer cold weather and active sports such as snowboarding, skating and checkers. You can be timid, though, so go ahead and take some chances. Try some solid food, for example.

33–36 Doughnuts. You are a supporter of law, order and lard. You've never met a fried food you didn't like. You have an inquiring mind — many times, you have wondered what happened to the holes.

37–40 A chocolate bar. You know how to live: up to your eyeballs in chocolate. That's what makes you so sweet!

WHICH KID'S BOOK CHARACTER ARE YOU?

Pick the statement that best describes you.

1. I prefer . . .
a. meat. > Go to question 2.
b. vegetables. > Go to question 3.

2. I am . . .
a. impulsive. > Go to question 4.
b. good at making plans. > Go to question 5.

3. I most enjoy . . .
a. playing sports. > Go to question 10.
b. helping people. > Go to question 11.

4. I consider myself . . .
a. the class clown. > Go to question 6.
b. loyal and affectionate. > You are Clifford the Big Red Dog.

5. I would most enjoy . . .
a. playing a practical joke. > Go to question 7.
b. relaxing in luxury. > Go to question 8.

6. I laugh most at . . .
a. gross jokes. > You are Walter the Farting Dog.
b. slapstick, like clowns slipping on banana peels. > You are Gloria, Officer Buckle's Dog.

7. I prefer . . .
a. silence! > You are the Grinch.
b. a wild party. > You are the Cat in the Hat.

8. If I had extra money, I would spend it on . . .
a. dinner in a fancy restaurant. > You are the Big Bad Wolf.
b. gold and diamonds. > Go to question 9.

series by H. Becker — available at your local bookstore!

b. track and field. > You are Percy Jackson.

9. I would prefer to travel . . .
a. in a luxury limo with a hot tub. > You are Greg Heffley.
b. on one of the fastest sailing ships on the ocean. > You are Captain Hook.

10. I prefer games that . . .
a. are fast and full of action. > Go to question 12.
b. require fast thinking and strategy. > Go to question 13.

11. If I had a choice between desserts, I'd pick . . .
a. fresh apple pie with vanilla ice cream. > Go to question 15.
b. triple fudge cake. > Go to question 16.

12. I prefer . . .
a. hockey. > You are Reese McSkittles from the Looney Bay All-Stars. What's that? You say you've never heard of Reese? You don't know what you're missing! Rush out right now and buy the entire Looney Bay All-Stars

13. I generally . . .
a. like to follow the rules. > You are Franklin the Turtle.
b. don't try to break the rules, but I seem to find myself in trouble anyway! > Go to question 14.

14. I prefer the colour . . .
a. red. > You are Bunnicula.
b. yellow. > you are Geronimo Stilton.

15. I most resemble . . .
a. a cylinder. > You are the Very Hungry Caterpillar.
b. a circle. > You are Winnie the Pooh.
c. a skinny rectangle. > You are Flat Stanley.

16. The clothes make the man, right?
a. Yes, I work hard to get my look right. > Go to question 17.
b. As long as I don't have to wear my cousin's hand-me-downs, I don't care too much about what I wear. > You are Harry Potter.

17. My most important item of clothing is . . .
a. my hat. > You are Willy Wonka.
b. my boxers. > You are Captain Underpants.

WHAT YOUR CHARACTER SAYS ABOUT YOU

Big Bad Wolf. You dream of being a chef. You would have a restaurant that serves nothing but pork: pork chops, pork sausages, pork and beans. Visit the dentist regularly; that'll help with your breath.

Bunnicula. People may comment on the size of your teeth. You are smart, with a taste for adventure and lettuce.

Captain Hook. You need to relax a bit. You are always in a hurry and fear that time is running out. You also have a snappy fashion sense and your loyal friends look up to you.

Captain Underpants. In brief, you have trouble following orders. Consider a career as a boxer or jockey.

The Cat in the Hat. Your favourite holiday is Halloween. You have a talent for getting noticed and might consider a career in public relations, advertising or fashion. You love poetry and enjoy pigs in wigs, pollywogs in bogs and kittens in mittens.

Clifford the Big Red Dog. You stand out in a crowd and you are very bright. You like to live large — your philosophy is go big or go home. You are a very loyal friend, but remember, nobody likes to be slobbered on.

Flat Stanley. You tend to bend under pressure. Other people may try to put you down, but you know how to stand up for yourself.

Franklin the Turtle. You are fast on the uptake, but slow to leap into action. Don't be afraid to come out of your shell and show the world the real you.

Geronimo Stilton. You like to read, write stories and eat cheese. You tend to get yourself into tight spots, but always manage to avoid punishment by a whisker. Small-minded people annoy you.

Greg Heffley. You have many talents to draw upon. You are not as wimpy as you think, but you may need to be a little nicer to your friends.

The Grinch. You tend to push others away before they can reject you. Try opening up your heart a bit, and, instead of being green with envy, you can grow and do much good in the world.

Harry Potter. You think there is more to this world than a lot of people see. You're a wiz at solving problems. You are very fortunate to have really great, loyal friends who have your back, just as much as you have theirs.

Officer Buckle's Dog, Gloria. You have a lot of charisma, and people can't help but notice you. Friends may be jealous of your talent, so try to understand and let them take centre stage once in a while. After a great performance, don't forget to bow (wow, you're good).

Percy Jackson. You sure know how to keep a secret. Don't let family troubles get you down. Be kind to animals — they are your friends.

Reese McSkittles. You are a natural athlete, good at every sport you try. You can be very resourceful, especially when faced with mummies wielding basketballs, gladiators with a grudge or smelly pirates.

The Very Hungry Caterpillar. You have the ability to transform ordinary things into works of art. You give 100% effort to every task, and nothing can sway you from your goals. Someday, you will surprise the world with your genius.

Walter the Farting Dog. You have a very sensitive digestive system. However, nothing gets you down. You love to participate in games of all sorts, especially if there is a ball involved. You are so active all day, you are usually dog-tired at bedtime.

Willy Wonka. You never follow the crowd. You have a sweet tooth. You will succeed in business.

Winnie the Pooh. You don't think of yourself as being very smart, but you are — you have a knack for solving problems, especially if they involve honey. People think you are fun to be with. When you fall on tough times, you just grin and bear it.

ARE YOU A SKATER?

1. What's an ollie?
a. A way to pop your skateboard in the air.
b. A way to ride down steps.
c. A type of stance — left foot forward.
d. The name of a skateboard manufacturer.

2. Which of the following is not part of a skateboard?
a. Deck
b. Trucks
c. Bearings
d. Switchplate

3. What does it mean to "go vert?"
a. Fall on your face.
b. Turn a complete 360 degrees in the air.
c. Do tricks in the air, like on a ramp or half-pipe.
d. Bomb down the middle of the street in traffic.

4. Where did skateboarding start?
a. West 49th Street in New York City
b. Australia
c. Ohio
d. California

5. What is a goofy stance?
a. A beginning rider, a newb.
b. Riding with your right foot forward.
c. Riding with your left foot forward.
d. Someone who pretends to not like skateboarding.

6. Which is not a skateboard trick?
a. Grind
b. Shove-it
c. 180
d. Braker Joe

19

7. Longboards are mostly used for . . .
a. doing tricks on half-pipes.
b. doing street tricks.
c. a means of transportation.
d. doing aerial tricks.

8. Skateboarders commonly break . . .
a. wrists.
b. hips.
c. wind.
d. rules.

9. Where's North America's largest free skate park?
a. Toronto
b. Los Angeles
c. Calgary
d. Nashville

10. The harder your skateboard wheels . . .
a. the faster you'll go.
b. the more control you will have.
c. the easier it is to carve turns.
d. the fancier and more expensive your board is.

YOU ARE . . .

0–2 Newbie. You are new to the world of skateboarding. No worries! You'll pick up the sport in a jiffy once you get started. Just take it easy on the tricks until you have the skills.

3–5 Ollie-Oop. You're pretty savvy when it comes to board games. Now it's time to take it to the street!

6–8 Going Pro. You know the difference between a kick-flip and a shove-it, a grind and a grab. Now put your know-how to use on park ramps and pipes!

9–10 Ryan Sheckler. You're the schoolyard pro — the ace who knows all of the lingo and all of the moves. You're living and breathing the sport! Keep up the good work — just a few more years of practice and you'll be a skateboard superstar.

WHAT'S YOUR INNER SPORT PERSONALITY?

Are you a hockey player deep down, or are you really a tennis expert? Take this quiz to find out which sport best represents your personal style and goals.

1. Your favourite seasons are . . .
a. spring and summer. > Go to question 2.
b. fall and winter. > Go to question 3.
c. I like them all. > Go to question 4.

2. On a super hot day, what do you prefer to do?
a. Chill on the sofa in an air-conditioned room. > Go to question 6.
b. Run through the sprinkler. > Go to question 10.
c. Do cannonballs into a swimming pool. > Go to question 3.

3. Which would you enjoy most?
a. Speeding super fast down a snowy hill. > Go to question 8.
b. Watching an exciting competition. > Go to question 9.

4. How would you describe yourself?
a. Quick-thinking and intense. > Go to question 5.

b. Outgoing and sociable. > Go to question 10.
c. Steady, decisive, determined. > Go to question 7.

5. Which words best describe you?
a. Traditional and conservative. > Your inner sport personality is Tennis.
b. Wild and crazy. > Your inner sport personality is Lacrosse.
c. Strong-willed and focused. > Go to question 6.

6. You prefer . . .
a. competing against others. > Your inner sport personality is Golf.
b. competing against yourself. > Go to question 7.

7. What's your favourite colour?
a. Black. > Your inner sport personality is Snowboarding.
b. Green. > Your inner sport personality is Track and Field.

8. When you grow up, you'd like to be . . .
a. famous. > Go to question 11.
b. rich. > Go to question 10.
c. happy. > Go to question 6.

9. Which meal would you prefer?
a. Turkey with all the trimmings. > Your inner sport personality is Football.
b. A nice juicy hot dog with chips. > Go to question 10.

10. Which statement best represents you?
a. I don't like to rock the boat. > Your inner sport personality is Baseball.

b. I like to do my own thing. > Your inner sport personality is Soccer.

11. Which do you prefer?
a. Hot cocoa. > Your inner sport personality is Hockey.
b. Ice-cold pop. > Your inner sport personality is Basketball.

WHAT YOUR INNER SPORT PERSONALITY REVEALS ABOUT YOU

Baseball. You take pride in your accomplishments. You prefer the simple things in life. No one can give you the runaround.

Basketball. You're smart and quick on your feet. People look up to you.

Football. You're not afraid to tackle big problems. When someone gets on your case, tell them to take a hike.

Golf. You know what you want and not even a trap could hold you back from getting it.

Hockey. You're a go-getter, and you know that if you practice hard and stay determined, you'll reach your goals no matter what.

Lacrosse. You get along well with others, except when you are feeling cross. Then you can be a real stick-in-the-mud.

Snowboarding. You like nothing better than the rush of adrenalin you get when you're moving fast. If nothing exciting is happening, you'll make it happen!

Soccer. You are passionate and powerful. You know there's no point in waiting for someone to give you a shot — you've just got to take it.

Tennis. You are a loyal and trustworthy friend. Life is all about the give and take. You know that sometimes you have to serve others, not just be served.

Track and Field. You don't let life's hurdles get you down. You've got what it takes to go the distance. When you spot a good opportunity, you jump on it.

COULD YOU WIN THE GOLD?

How well do you know the Olympics? Do you know its history, which sports are included and what the rules are? Test your knowledge and find out if you are a gold medallist in sports trivia or an also-ran at random facts.

1. What did competitors in the first Olympics wear?
a. Fig leaves
b. Togas
c. Nothing
d. Shorts and T-shirts

2. What was the first year that women competed for a medal in ice hockey?
a. 1920
b. 1998
c. 1948
d. 1980

3. Which of the following was once an Olympic sport?
a. Arm wrestling
b. Sky diving
c. Pigeon shooting
d. Mud wrestling

4. Which phrase is the motto of the Olympics?
a. Swifter, higher, stronger.
b. I came, I saw, I conquered.
c. Reach for the top.
d. We are all Olympians.

5. Between 1920 and 2006, how many gold medals did Canada's men's Olympic hockey team win?
a. 10
b. 2
c. 11
d. 7

6. Jamaica is celebrated for sending which team to the Olympics?
a. Bobsled team
b. Speed skating team
c. Sumo wrestling team
d. Hockey team

7. Which Olympian ran a race barefoot?
a. Mark Spitz
b. Jesse Owens
c. Zola Budd
d. Nadia Comaneci

8. Which Olympic gymnast was the first to score a perfect ten?
a. Olga Korbut
b. Nadia Comaneci
c. Zola Budd
d. Mary Lou Retton

9. The Iron Cross is performed in what sport?
a. Weightlifting
b. Decathlon
c. Men's gymnastics
d. Men's trampoline

10. The Clean and Jerk is performed in what sport?
a. Weightlifting
b. Decathlon
c. Men's gymnastics
d. Men's trampoline

11. Which Japanese city has never hosted the Olympics?
a. Nagano
b. Sapporo
c. Tokyo
d. Osaka

12. Which sport includes an event called the butterfly?
a. Figure skating
b. Swimming
c. Rhythmic gymnastics
d. Weightlifting

13. How many different events are there in the decathlon?
a. 12
b. 10
c. 6
d. 2

14. Mark Tewksbury won a gold medal for Canada in 1992 in what sport?
a. Alpine skiing
b. Swimming
c. Triathlon
d. Diving

15. Which Canadian runner held the world record for the 100 m sprint in track and field in 1996?
a. Simon Whitfield
b. Ben Johnson
c. Donovan Bailey
d. Bruny Surin

16. Which two cities have never hosted the Olympics?
a. Calgary and Edmonton
b. Quebec City and Montreal
c. Toronto and Montreal
d. Toronto and Quebec City

17. Canada won the Olympic gold medal for men's ice hockey in 2002. Which player was NOT on the team?
a. Eric Lindros
b. Curtis Joseph
c. Mike Peca
d. Brett Hull

18. Which sport have Canadians won the most medals for?
a. Hockey
b. Speed skating
c. Track and Field
d. Swimming

19. The first person to win a gold medal in snowboarding was a Canadian. Who was he?
a. Gaetan Boucher
b. Ross Rebagliati
c. Duff Gibson
d. David Pelletier

20. What city hosted the 2006 Olympic games?
a. Calgary
b. Beijing
c. Turin
d. Salt Lake City

WHAT'S YOUR ULTIMATE SPORTS CAR?

1. You're all about . . .
a. the looks.
b. the speed and power.
c. the impress 'em all price tag.

2. If you had to choose, your ultimate car would be . . .
a. black.
b. orange.
c. red.

3. While driving your dream machine, you would prefer

to wear . . .
a. shorts and a T-shirt.
b. a leather jacket and shades.
c. a tie and blazer.

4. Your favourite snack is . . .
a. a Big Gulp from 7-11.
b. a Blizzard.
c. oysters on the half shell.

5. Which appeals to you most:
a. Driving along the coast of California and taking a break at a beach to surf.
b. Bombing along country roads past cornfields.
c. Taking the twists and turns of the Italian alps at high speed, but with perfect control.

SCORING

1. a1 b2 c10	3. a1 b5 c10	5. a1 b3 c10
2. a1 b2 c10	4. a1 b10 c5	

28

YOUR DREAM SPORTS CAR IS A . . .

5–10 Shelby Mustang GT 500. You're all about the attitude. You want a muscle car that will tell the world you've got it made in the shade. No one's gonna show you up. No one's even gonna dare.

11–15 Corvette Z06. This car shows your can-do style to best advantage. One day you're living the high life, the next, rocking out with your buddies on the back porch, jamming on your six-string.

16–20 Porsche 911 GT3. This car is like a killer whale — clean lines, great profile and not an animal to take for granted. No wonder this car is the one for you. Like that orca, when you're ready to strike out, you're just as focused, intense and 100% determined to succeed.

21–29 Jaguar XKR 5.0. You prefer proven performers over the latest fad. This car screams "money and style." It can take you absolutely everywhere you want to go, and you'll always be respected and admired.

30–39 Ferrari FXX Evolution. Can you say, "Cheese?" You love the spotlight, and there's nothing more glam than this dream-on-wheels, with you in the driver's seat. The paparazzi will chase you everywhere!

40+ Lamborghini Murcielago. You deserve the best, don't you? This regal roadster is the perfect vehicle for your superiorness. Mere mortals will bow to you — as they should.

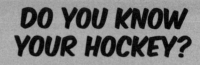

DO YOU KNOW YOUR HOCKEY?

1. Who is the all-time leading NHL scorer (during the regular season)?
a. Gordie Howe
b. Wayne Gretzky
c. Brett Hull
d. Mario Lemieux

2. What was "Rocket" Richard's real first name?
a. Morris
b. Manny
c. Maurice
d. Malcolm

3. Which team has won the most Stanley Cups?
a. Montreal
b. Toronto
c. Detroit
d. New York

4. Which team was originally located in Quebec City and named the Nordiques?
a. Dallas Stars
b. Tampa Bay Lightning
c. Colorado Avalanche
d. Carolina Hurricanes

5. Which team has won the THIRD most Stanley Cups?
a. Montreal
b. Toronto
c. Detroit
d. New York

6. How many NHL teams were there at the start?
a. 8
b. 12
c. 5
d. 9

7. Which team was *not* one of the "Original Six" NHL teams?
a. Boston Bruins
b. Chicago Blackhawks
c. Montreal Canadiens
d. Buffalo Sabres

8. How many NHL teams were there in 1996–1997?

a. 25

b. 26

c. 30

d. 40

9. How fast can a puck hit by one of the best NHL shooters travel?

a. About 100 km/hr

b. About 150 km/hr

c. About 100 miles/hr

d. About 1000 ft/second

10. Gordie Howe was given the Hart Memorial Trophy, for being the most valuable player, how many times in his career?

a. 6

b. 7

c. 5

d. 2

11. Why was the Stanley Cup series cancelled in 1919?

a. World War II had broken out.

b. There was a flu epidemic.

c. There was a riot in Montreal.

d. The Depression.

12. Who holds the record for the hardest shot in the NHL?

a. Evgeni Malkin

b. Wayne Gretzky

c. Zdeno Chara

d. Alex Ovechkin

13. In what year did hockey become an Olympic event?

a. 1920

b. 1940

c. 1960

d. 1980

14. Who holds the record for playing on the most NHL teams?

a. Al Iafrate

b. Mike Sillinger

c. Michel Petit

d. J.J. Daigneault

15. Which of the following is not the nickname of an NHL player?

a. Super Mario

b. Cujo

c. Peter Puck

d. The Dominator

SCORING

Give yourself a point for
each correct answer.

1.	b	9.	c
2.	c	10.	a
3.	a	11.	b
4.	c	12.	c
5.	c	13.	a
6.	c	14.	b
7.	d	15.	c
8.	b		

YOU ARE . . .

1–3 In the crease. You're sharpening your skate knowledge every day!

4–8 On a breakaway! You've got a solid grip on the game!

9–11 A power player! You really know your stuff.

12–15 The star of the game! You are totally up on the NHL!

DO YOU HAVE WHAT IT TAKES TO SURVIVE?

1. You have fallen into quicksand! What do you do?
a. Cry for mommy.
b. When the crocodiles come to eat me, I'll grab one by the tail and pull myself out.
c. Relax and allow myself to float gently to the top, keeping an eye out for hungry vultures.
d. Flail my arms wildly to keep from sinking into the deadly goop.

2. You are skating on a frozen pond when you hear the ice crack. What do you do?
a. Keep skating. Ice and snow always make weird sounds.
b. Immediately head to shore.
c. Jump up and down to see if the ice is safe where I am.
d. Head toward the middle of the pond where the ice is thicker.

3. Avalanche! How will you stay alive?
a. By making swimming motions to try and stay on top and get out of its path.
b. By holding up my ski poles to act as a flag for rescuers.
c. By digging to create an air pocket around me.
d. By holding my breath.

4. You are out hiking and realize you've forgotten your lunch. A venomous snake crosses your path. Next thing you know, it strikes! What do you do?
a. Kill it and eat it.
b. Put ice on the bite site to slow the spread of venom. Then kill the snake and eat it.
c. Suck out the venom from the wound, then go for help.
d. Wash out the wound as best I can and try and get help.

5. Your lifeboat has been swamped with no land in sight! What do you do?
a. Take off my clothes so they don't drag me down and tread water.
b. Grab onto something that is floating and stay as still as possible until help comes.
c. Cry for mommy.
d. Swim for shore.

6. You are out walking in the middle of nowhere when a major lightning storm hits. What do you do?
a. Take shelter under the tallest tree.
b. Submerge myself in the closest bog or swamp.
c. Crouch down into a small ball.
d. Take photographs — it's a totally awesome storm!

7. You are lost in the sweltering desert. You are hungry and thirsty, with no help in sight. You have a little food and water. What do you do?
a. Eat.
b. Drink my water.
c. Neither eat nor drink.
d. Both eat and drink.

8. A shark is *attacking* you! What do you do?
a. Punch it in the nose.
b. Swim away — fast!
c. Stay quiet and hope it forgets me soon.
d. Most sharks are really gentle, so it could make a great photo opportunity.

9. Your whole family has been turned into zombies. What do you do?
a. Well, if I can't beat them, might as well join them.
b. Take the family car and head for a diner in a small desert town.
c. Arm myself with a club and thwack anyone that comes near me.
d. Run upstairs where there's no exit — zombies can't climb, right?

10. Cannibals are chasing you! How do you escape?

a. Invite them to share my homemade lunch of wild boar stew and English trifle. They'd love the change in their ho-hum(an) diet.

b. Immobilize them with a poison dart I'd concoct from nearby vines, sticks and toad juice.

c. Radio for help and sit tight until the SWAT team arrived — I'm in downtown Saskatoon, after all.

d. Ask them who did their hair and makeup.

SCORING
Give yourself a point for everything you got right.

1. c	6. c
2. b	7. b
3. a	8. a
4. d	9. c
5. b	10. b

WHAT ARE YOUR SURVIVAL CHANCES?

1–3 Lock the doors and hide! Your chances of making it through an extreme event are slim. Make sure you always surround yourself with big, strong, competent friends to improve your odds of making it to adulthood.

4–6 In shock, but conscious. You can manage some of the more common disasters (exploding microwave, attack hamster, teenage girl invasion) with style. But use caution whenever you leave your yard.

7–8 Limping, but upright. You are tough as nails — ones polished a bewitching shade of Go-Go Guava. You are also smart and a lightning fast thinker — important when the clouds are raining hand grenades and slimy prehistoric creatures are emerging from the soil like bubbling lava.

9–10 Last man standing. You have what it takes to survive an alien invasion, a nuclear holocaust, a horde of man-eating locusts and a volcanic eruption all at once. Beef up your library and DVD collection for when you are the last man on earth. It's gonna get lonely.

DO YOU HAVE EAGLE EYES?

DO YOU HAVE 20/20 VISION?

This test will give you an eye-dea of how clear your vision is. It's based on the Snellen Eye Chart. The chart is placed on a brightly lit wall. You'll stand 20 feet (610 cm) away from it. The line you can read tells you whether or not your vision is "normal." This means that what you can see from 20 feet away is what a typical person can see from 20 feet away (20/20). If you can only see at 20 feet what a typical person can see from 100 feet away, your vision would be 20/100. You would need to wear glasses to help you see better.

A portion of the Snellen Eye Chart is reproduced here. You'll have to photocopy it onto a flat piece of 11 x 17 paper at 205%. To check that it's the right size, make sure the E on the top line measures 88 mm high. Note: To fit the page, we deleted a few lines from our test.

To do the test you will need:
• A friend
• A small piece of tape, push pin or other fastener to attach the sheet to a wall
• A measuring tape
• A photocopier

1. With the measuring tape, measure off 20 feet (610 cm) from the wall.

2. Mark the spot so you can stand or sit there to do the test.

3. Have your friend attach the chart to the wall at eye level.

4. Cover your left eye. Starting with the largest letters at the top of the chart, read each row in order. Your friend should stand close enough to the chart to see each letter clearly, and make sure you are reading them correctly.

5. Make a note of which line is the last one you can read without making more than one mistake.

6. Repeat with the other eye; it may have a different score.

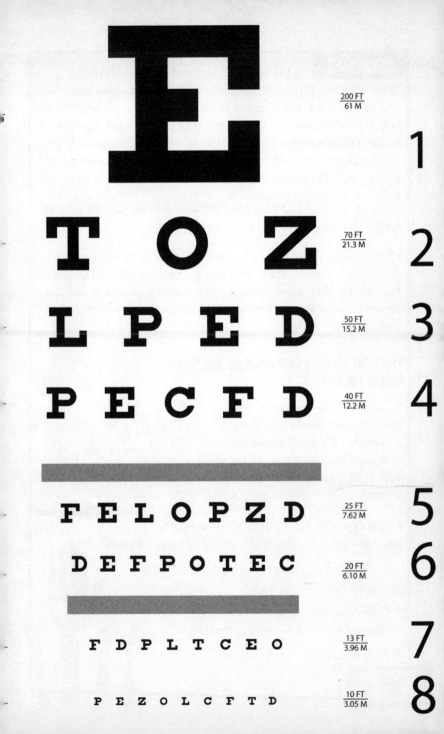

E	$\frac{200\ \text{FT}}{61\ \text{M}}$ — 1
T O Z	$\frac{70\ \text{FT}}{21.3\ \text{M}}$ — 2
L P E D	$\frac{50\ \text{FT}}{15.2\ \text{M}}$ — 3
P E C F D	$\frac{40\ \text{FT}}{12.2\ \text{M}}$ — 4
F E L O P Z D	$\frac{25\ \text{FT}}{7.62\ \text{M}}$ — 5
D E F P O T E C	$\frac{20\ \text{FT}}{6.10\ \text{M}}$ — 6
F D P L T C E O	$\frac{13\ \text{FT}}{3.96\ \text{M}}$ — 7
P E Z O L C F T D	$\frac{10\ \text{FT}}{3.05\ \text{M}}$ — 8

SCORING

• The "scores" for this test are written at the left of each line. If you can read the bottom line with either eye, your score for that eye would be 20/15, which means that what the typical person can only read at 15 feet away, you can see from 20 feet away. In other words, you are far-sighted — able to see better from a distance than most other people in that eye. It is quite common for young people to be far-sighted.

• If you can only read the second line from the bottom, your vision is normal. You can see about as well as most people.

• If you can only read the line that is third or fourth from the bottom, you are near-sighted. This means that you must be closer to an object than most people to see it clearly. If this is where you score, you should consider asking your parents about getting a more accurate eye test from a professional.

DO YOU HAVE EYES ON THE BACK OF YOUR HEAD?

Peripheral (puh-RIF-fur-rull) means side. This test checks how well you can see out of the sides of your eyes. How wide of a space you can see when both eyes are open is called your field of vision.

1. Close your left eye. Stretch both of your arms out to the side, shoulder height, with your fingers pointed.

2. Slowly bring your arms to the front. Stop moving an arm when you first see its hand.

3. Note the position your arms are in, and compare it against the diagrams that follow.

4. Repeat with your right eye closed.

DO YOU HAVE NERVES OF STEEL?

Nerves bring messages from different parts of your body back and forth to your brain. Try these tests to find out how well your nervous system is doing its job!

You will need a partner to help you with most of these tests and to keep track of how you do. Make sure you help test him too!

1. Eye Movement Test

Three different nerves control how well your eyes track a moving object. To do this test, have your partner hold up one finger about 30 cm in front of you. Keep your head still and your eyes fixed on his fingertip.

Have your partner move his finger up, then down, then to the left and the right.

Did both eyes accurately follow the movement of the fingertip?

2. Pupil Reaction Test

Your pupils — the dark spots in the middle of your eyes — grow and shrink depending on the amount of light they're exposed to. When you are in a bright location, the pupils shrink, becoming very small and letting less light into your eyes. In a dim location, the pupils will grow to let more light in.

To test your pupils' reaction to changing light, go into a small windowless room, such as a bathroom. Turn the light off. After a minute, have your friend come in and immediately turn on the light. He should study your eyes to see how they react to the change in light.

Did the pupils in both eyes rapidly shrink?

Now, leave the door open but turn off the light again. The room should be dim, but not completely dark. Have your partner continue to study your pupils.

Did the pupils slowly expand in the dimmer light?

3. Knee Jerk Reflex

This test tells you if messages are being properly sent from your leg muscles to your spinal cord.

To do this test, sit with your legs crossed so that the top leg can swing freely. Using the side of his hand (like a karate chop), have your friend lightly hit your leg just below your knee cap.

Did the leg immediately kick?

4. Babinski Reflex Test

This test also checks for proper function of the nervous system.

To do the test, have your partner gently stroke the sole of your foot or do it yourself.

Did the big toe curl up?

5. Startle Reflex Test

To do this test, your friend will have to surprise you by making a loud, sudden noise at some point during the day.

At the sound, did you twitch, move your head, blink, throw your hands in the air, jump, scream, or in any other way react in a sudden sharp motion to the noise?

6. Hypoglossal Nerve Test

The hypoglossal nerve controls the motion of your tongue.

To do this test, stick out your tongue and move it side to side.

Did the tongue move smoothly in all directions?

RESULTS

0–2 Hello . . . is there anybody in there?
3–4 Potential zombie.
5–7 Nerves of steel!

HOW NERVY ARE YOU?

Here's a test to discover how far apart the sensory receptors are in different parts of your body.

To do these tests, you will need a partner, two sharpened pencils and a ruler.

Instructions
1. Remove your shirt.
2. Turn your back to your partner.
3. Have your partner *lightly* touch your back with both pencil points. The tips should be about 20 cm apart. Can you feel the two pencils?
4. Have your partner touch your back again with the pencils, but this time, bring them about 1 cm closer together. Can you still feel the two pencil points?
5. Continue bringing the pencils closer and closer together. There will come a point when you can no longer feel two distinct points — it will feel like only one pencil is touching you!
6. Tell your friend when you can only feel one touch. Have him measure and record the distance between the two pencils. This distance indicates how far apart the sensory receptors are in the skin on this part of your back.
7. With your eyes closed, repeat these steps on different parts of your body, such as your upper arm, stomach, leg and fingers. Record the pencil distances for each area.

Body Part	Distance at which you cannot distinguish two touches
Upper back	
Lower back	
Upper arm	
Wrist	
Leg	
Index finger (inside)	
Index finger (outside)	
Top of foot	
Sole of foot	

Where are the sensory receptors closest together? Where are they farthest apart? What does this test show you about which parts of your body are more or less sensitive to touch?

You can also compare your results with those of your friends. Who has the highest scores? The least? It doesn't mean you're better or worse than anyone, it's just interesting to see and learn where we're the most sensitive.

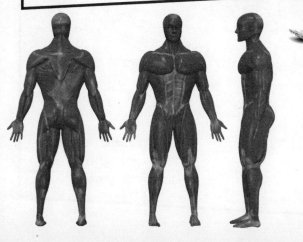

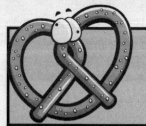

ARE YOU A HUMAN PRETZEL?

Here are some simple tests to determine if you're double-jointed.

Being double-jointed does not mean you have an extra joint in any part of your body. The term refers to a joint that is more flexible than is typical in most people. Many people have a few joints that are unusually flexible. But not as many people are extremely flexible in many joints.

Answer yes or no to the following questions:

1. Can you touch your left thumb to the inside of your left wrist?

2. Can you touch your right thumb to the inside of your right wrist?

3. Can you straighten your arms so that your elbows point in instead of out?

4. Can you straighten your legs so your knees flex backwards?

5. Can you bend the four fingers on your right hand so they flex backwards?

7. Can you flex your right ankle up at an extreme angle?

6. Can you bend the four fingers on your left hand so they flex backwards?

8. Can you flex your left ankle at an extreme angle?

9. Can you bend just the top joint of any one finger, while the rest of the finger is straight?

10. Can you stretch your arms above you and wrap one around your neck?

11. Can you wrap either leg around your neck?

12. Can you twist or bend any other joint in your body in an unusual or extreme way?

SCORING

If you answered yes to one or more of these questions, it means that you have at least one very flexible joint. Give yourself a point for each yes.

RESULTS

2–4 Double Trouble! You can freak out your friends with your extreme joint sports.

5–8 Rubber-band man! You are extremely twistable and twisted.

9–12 Contortionist! Have you considered a career in the circus?

HOW FIT ARE YOU?

Are you superhero tough or marshmallow material? We come in all different shapes and sizes, but it's always important to be fit. Being fit helps you get through the day with more energy and helps you stay healthy.

To find out how you stack up, do each of these tests. Then combine your scores in the summary table at the end of this section to get an overall fitness total.

Note: If you are not familiar with these activities, or if you do not exercise regularly, do these tests with adult supervision.

Test 1, Upper Body Strength — the Push-up

You will need:
A friend
A stopwatch or clock with a second hand

To do a push-up, lie face down on the floor. Put your palms on the floor just below your shoulders. Keeping your body straight, like a plank, push into the floor with your arms to raise yourself off the floor. Do not arch your back or bend your knees.

Do as many push-ups as you can in one minute, without losing the proper form.

SCORING   Start with the number of push-ups you did. If you're older than 10, subtract 1 push-up for every year you're over 10. If you're younger than 10, add 1 to your total. For example, if you are 8 years old and did 18 push-ups, add one to your total to give you a score of 19. If you are 11, and you did 18 push-ups, take away 1, which will give you a score of 17.

Look at the chart below to determine your final score. Put that score in the summary table at the end of these tests.

Less than 7. Needs improvement	Put a 4 in the summary table
7–20. Good on ya! Healthy fitness achieved!	Put a 6 in the summary table
21–26. High fives! High fitness level!	Put an 8 in the summary table
27+. Superstar Athlete!	Put a 10 in the summary table

Test 2, Upper Body Strength — the Chin-up

You will need:
A friend
A stopwatch or clock with a second hand
A chin up bar, or another strongly hung horizontal bar, placed high enough so that your feet aren't touching the ground

To do a chin-up, begin by hanging from the bar using an underhand grip (so the palms of your hands face you). Using only your arms — do not kick or jerk your body — pull yourself up toward the bar. Your chin should be able to go above the bar. Do as many chin-ups as you can — without losing your form, kicking or jerking your body — in one minute.

SCORING Start with the number of chin-ups you did.

If you are older than 10, subtract 1 chin-up for every year that you are older. If you are younger than 10, add 1 to your number.

Look at the chart below to determine your final score. Put that score in the summary table at the end of the tests.

0. Needs improvement	Put a 4 in the summary table
1–2. Good on ya! Healthy fitness achieved!	Put a 6 in the summary table
3–8. High fives! High fitness level!	Put an 8 in the summary table
9+. Superstar athlete!	Put a 10 in the summary table

Test 3, Core Strength — the Sit-up

You will need:

A friend

A stopwatch or clock with a second hand

To do a sit-up, lie on your back with your hands clasped behind your neck. Bend your knees and put the soles of your feet on the floor. Your heels should be no more than 30 cm from your bum. Curl your torso up until your elbows touch your knees. Then lower yourself back down. Be sure not to pull on your neck with your hands — they are not there to pull you up. Do as many sit-ups as you can in one minute.

SCORING Start with the number of sit-ups you did. If you are older than 10, subtract 2 for every year you are older. If you are younger than 10, add 2 to your number.

Look at the chart below to determine your final score. Put that score in the summary table at the end of the tests.

Less than 33. Needs improvement	Put a 4 in the summary table
34-39. Good on ya! Healthy fitness achieved!	Put a 6 in the summary table
40-49. High fives! High fitness level!	Put an 8 in the summary table
50+. Superstar Athlete!	Put a 10 in the summary table

Test 4, Aerobic Fitness — Run in Place

You will need:

A stopwatch or clock with a second hand

To do the test, run in place, jump rope or do jumping jacks for three minutes. At the end of three minutes, describe how you feel.

SCORING Look at the chart below to determine your final score. Put that score in the summary table at the end of the tests.

Stopped before the 3 minutes were up. Needs improvement	Put a 4 in the summary table
Heart pounding, exhausted. Good on ya! Healthy fitness level achieved	Put a 6 in the summary table
A little breathless but okay. High fives	Put an 8 in the summary table
Barely broke a sweat. Superstar athlete!	Put a 10 in the summary table

Test 5, Balance Test — Standing On One Leg

You will need:
A friend
A stopwatch or clock with a second hand.

Close your eyes. Lift one foot off the floor by bending your knee. Remain standing on one foot as long as possible. Repeat two more times. Then do the test three times on the other foot.

SCORING Use your best time for scoring.

Look at the chart below to determine your final score. Put that score in the summary table at the end of the tests.

Less than 12 seconds. Weeble	Put a 4 in the summary table
12–23 seconds. Dreidel	Put a 6 in the summary table
24–29 seconds. Stork	Put an 8 in the summary table
More than 30 seconds. Rock	Put a 10 in the summary table

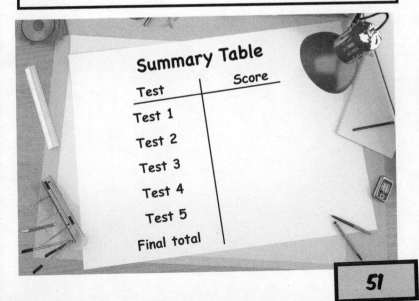

Summary Table

Test	Score
Test 1	
Test 2	
Test 3	
Test 4	
Test 5	
Final total	

OVERALL SCORE Add up your scores from the five fitness tests. Compare your total to the scores here.

20–29 Gear grinder. You would benefit from more activity in your day. It's important to find something you like — maybe being part of a team would get you out more, like playing soccer or baseball. Or maybe you'd prefer something more solitary, like running or bike riding. Get active for at least ten minutes at a time, four times a day.

30–39 Primed for action. Your fitness level is good. You can build strength and stamina by playing a wider variety of sports and practicing your skills everyday. Work up a sweat for at least twenty minutes, three times a day to increase your fitness power.

40–50 Star athlete. You've got excellent strength and stamina. Build on this solid base by increasing the time you engage in physical activity to an hour or more every day. You'll do great in any sport you work at.

HOW HONEST ARE YOU?

1. You observe someone kicking a ball over the fence during recess. Later, when the owner is looking for it what do you do?

a. Tell him where the ball is, but not how it got there.

b. Tell him who kicked the ball over the fence.

c. Tell him who kicked the ball over the fence, as long as it's not your friend or the school bully.

d. Say you haven't seen it, just to see how long it takes for him to find it.

2. You forgot to do your homework last night. What do you do?

a. Ask your dad to write you a note with an excuse.

b. Tell the teacher you couldn't do it because you had a family commitment.

c. Tell the teacher you forgot to do your homework.

d. Don't say anything and hope your teacher forgets to collect it.

3. You find a wallet with a $20 bill in it near your house. There's no ID, but it probably belongs to one of your neighbours. What do you do?

a. Take the wallet house to house to see if you can find the owner.

b. Take out the $20, then take the empty wallet house to house to find the owner.

c. Take the $20 and throw out the wallet.

d. Put the wallet in your drawer. You'll give it back if you figure out who it belongs to.

4. A girl in your class asks if you like her new hairstyle. You think it looks ridiculous. What do you do?
a. Tell the truth, even if it hurts her feelings. Better than letting her go around looking like a doorknob.
b. Tell her she looks great.
c. Tell her its okay, but you preferred the old hairstyle.
d. Make a joke and avoid answering.

5. You got an A on a math test. When you look it over, you see the teacher made a mistake — your score should be a C! What do you do?
a. Nothing. That was a lucky break!
b. Nothing. But you wind up feeling guilty.
c. Tell your parents and let them decide how to handle the situation.
d. Tell the teacher she made a mistake.

6. A kid in your class is moving away. He asks you to keep in touch. You don't like him much and don't really want to. What do you say?
a. "Sure!" But you feel guilty because you probably won't.
b. "I'll try, but I'm not good at that sort of stuff."
c. "Sure!" Why make the guy feel bad?
d. "No, I don't think so. Sorry."

7. You accidentally broke a neighbour's window. Nobody saw you do it. You . . .
a. confess right away and promise to pay for the replacement glass.
b. tell your parents that you saw some kid break the window.
c. keep quiet and hope nobody asks you about it.
d. tell your parents you did it, but give a long explanation for how it wasn't really your fault.

8. You're playing tennis with a friend. The ball you hit lands just outside the line, but he doesn't see it. What do you do?

a. Nothing. If he didn't call it, it must have been in after all.

b. Nothing. Tough luck for him for not seeing it.

c. Shout, "Out!" and turn the ball over to your opponent.

d. Ask him, "Did you see that ball? It might have been out." Then let him decide if it was in or out.

SCORING

1. a2 b4 c3 d1
2. a0 b2 c4 d3

3. a4 b1 c0 d1
4. a4 b1 c2 d3
5. a1 b2 c3 d4

6. a2 b3 c1 d4
7. a4 b0 c2 d3
8. a2 b1 c4 d3

YOU ARE . . .

5–10 A slippery devil. You hate hurting people — especially if one of them is you! You don't really like lying . . . it's just that it's easier to fib than to make waves. Don't be so sure, though. Ask yourself this question: when the water gets rough, who will pull you out?

11–17 The waffler. It's all so confusing. What is a white lie anyway? And what if you know about something, but don't tell — does that count as a lie? Since you can't be sure, you leave the decisions to someone else — a friend, a parent or maybe even just fate. But what does that say about you?

18–27 True blue. You tell the truth most of the time. But you sometimes slip. Then you feel guilty. And that's the hard part: even if you get away with a lie, you wind up wishing you had told the truth! No one said being truthful is easy. It can be tricky, especially if you know being honest can hurt someone else's feelings. But keep up the good work — you're on the right track!

28–32 Too true? You have a keen sense of right and wrong and are not afraid to speak the truth. That's a terrific quality. But sometimes, you can be a bit blunt. You might want to consider not only what you say but how you say it.

WHAT ARE YOU BORN TO DO?

1. Your friend has been injured in an accident. What do you do?

a. Call 911 right away. > Go to question 2.

b. Find an adult who can help. > Go to question 3.

c. Get him in a comfortable position, and make sure he is warm and able to breathe comfortably. > Go to question 4.

d. Panic! > Go to question 8.

2. How would you describe yourself?

a. I'm shy, but curious. > Go to question 9.

b. I'm outgoing. > Go to question 8.

c. I'm down-to-earth. > Go to question 5.

3. What would you rather read?

a. A non-fiction how-to book. > Go to question 5.

b. A fantasy novel. > Go to question 10.

c. An adventure story with a strong hero. > Go to question 4.

4. You see your little sister crying over a broken toy. What do you do?

a. Immediately try to fix it. > Go to question 5.

b. Tell her to stop crying and get over it. > Go to question 6.

c. Put my arm around her and comfort her. > Go to question 7.

5. I prefer . . .

a. working with people. > You are a Leader.

b. working with my hands. > You are a Farmer.

c. working with ideas. > You are a Hunter.

6. Which statement best describes you?
a. I like being where the action is.
> You are an Entertainer.
b. I avoid the spotlight. > You are an Artist.
c. I thrive on competition. > You are a Warrior.

7. People describe you as . . .
a. gentle and kind. > You are a Healer.
b. a bit of a showoff. > You are an Entertainer.
c. creative and kooky. > You are an Artist.

8. If you had your choice of snacks, what would you pick?
a. A giant birthday cake, loaded with whipped cream, chocolate and three kinds of ice cream. > You are an Artist.
b. Nachos or popcorn, things I can share with my friends. > You are an Entertainer.
c. Fresh, delicious fruits and veggies. > You are a Farmer.

9. How would you prefer to spend your day?
a. Exploring deep woods. > You are a Hunter.
b. Exploring the countryside. > You are a Farmer.
c. Battling it out in the urban jungle. > You are a Warrior.

10. Which subject do you prefer?
a. Gym — especially when we play dodgeball. > You are a Warrior.
b. Math — I love solving problems. > You are a Hunter.
c. Social Studies — it's interesting learning about conquerors and explorers. > You are a Leader.

IF YOU ARE . . .

A Healer. You are gentle, caring and like to help people. You are a good listener and a good sport. In ancient times, you would have been known for your talent with healing herbs and spells. Good careers for you would be doctor, nurse, therapist, daycare worker or veterinarian.

An Entertainer. You like to be where the action is. Hundreds of years ago, you would have been a bard, telling stories and singing songs as you moved from place to place. Now you should consider a career that allows you to connect with people, like actor, singer, musician, sports star or newscaster.

A Warrior. You combine strength of character with physical strength and presence. You have courage, and you tackle challenges with enthusiasm. In ancient times, you would have been the first into battle, rallying others with your powerful personality and bravery. Possible careers: a lawyer, politician, military officer, police officer or firefighter.

An Artist. In ancient times, you might have communicated with the otherworld and transformed your spiritual knowledge into art, like cave paintings, dramatic dances or inspiring stories. Today, these same gifts come out in you as creative talent that speaks to people. Consider a career as a pastor, illustrator, writer or film director.

A Leader. You have excellent people skills. You can get others excited about a project, or calm down hotheads with just a few words. In ancient times, you would have been the tribal chief or king. Politician, social activist, teacher, coach, military officer or business executive are all good career choices for you.

A Farmer. You are level-headed, practical and good at planning. You enjoy working with your hands and being outdoors. In ancient times, you would have been a fisherman or farmer. Today, you can use your talents as a farmer, chef, environmental scientist or engineer.

A Hunter. You notice what other people don't, and you grasp complex ideas in a jiffy. You love to observe others and delight in solving problems. In ancient times, you would have been a hunter, an explorer or a trader. You would make an excellent detective, spy, accountant, store owner, entrepeneur or zoologist.

WHAT'S YOUR UNDERWEAR STYLE?

1. I would describe myself as . . .
a. quiet. I don't like to stand out in a crowd.
b. the life of the party.
c. creative and wild.
d. one of the guys.

2. I prefer . . .
a. darts.
b. football.
c. long distance running.
d. badminton or tennis.

3. My favourite type of food is . . .
a. anything spicy!
b. meat and potatoes.
c. Italian — cheesy goodness!
d. Asian — crunchy veggies and lots of interesting flavours.

4. If I were going on vacation, I'd love to . . .
a. go tubing.
b. ski.
c. explore a new place.
d. just chill.

5. I like to listen to . . .
a. country music.
b. punk/metal.
c. classical.
d. hip-hop.

6. I prefer the colour . . .
a. black.
b. purple.
c. red. No, green. No, orange.
d. I don't care much about what colour things are.

7. After school, I'd rather . . .
a. shoot hoops in the driveway with a friend.
b. watch TV.
c. play video games.
d. play a soccer game with my team.

8. I know the *most* about . . .
a. my favourite sport or team.
b. science or computers.
c. my favourite TV show or movie characters.
d. how to make people laugh.

60

Give yourself the following points for each answer. Add them up to get your results.

1. a1 b4 c3 d2
2. a1 b4 c2 d3
3. a5 b1 c2 d3
4. a4 b2 c3 d1

5. a2 b3 c1 d4
6. a2 b3 c4 d1
7. a3 b1 c2 d4
8. a3 b2 c1 d5

YOUR STYLE IS . . .

8–16 Tighty whities. You're not the kind of guy who likes to rock the boat. Keep it simple, you say. Who cares about what colour or pattern is on your undies? As long as they fit, that's all that matters.

17–24 Boxers. You love sports. That's why you're a straight-up boxer man — whether you're driving toward the net or racing toward the finish line, they're cool and comfortable. What more could a guy ask for?

25–29 Superhero briefs. You're cheerful and independent. So what if people think picture-pants are just for little kids? They're fun. Knowing you've got Spidey on your butt brightens your day.

30–34 Crazy boxers. You love to stand out in a crowd and get noticed. That's why you are a fan of the wildest, nuttiest boxers on the planet. And you love to let the waistband of your Mr. Peanuts or Happy Faces drawers show over the top of your pants. Why not share the giggles with your buds?

HOW WEIRD IS YOUR FAMILY?

1. Everyone in your family . . .
a. likes cereal for breakfast.
b. is very musical.
c. has hair on the soles of their feet.
d. is different from each other.

2. In your family, there are . . .
a. two antelopes and a llama.
b. a mom, a dad and a kid or two.
c. a mix of people — some half-relatives, some step-relatives, some just passing through.
d. twins.

3. A favourite family meal would be . . .
a. chicken and rice.
b. greasy grimy gopher guts.
c. eggplant parmesan.
d. blood.

4. At least one adult in your family has . . .
a. a mullet.
b. a job.
c. an aversion to sunlight.
d. two heads.

5. When you go out together as a family, people who see you together say . . .
a. "Aren't they a lovely looking family?"
b. "Don't make any sudden moves . . ."
c. "Are you sure you are all related?"
d. "Wow, you all look exactly alike — love the jumpsuits . . ."

6. Your mom . . .
a. has a box in the basement you are not allowed to touch. It smells really bad.
b. has a good sense of humour.
c. puts the garbage out in her robe.
d. mutters to herself, "I'll show them. One day, I'll show them."

7. At parent-teacher meetings, your teacher . . .

    a. is always happy to chat with your parents.
    b. is very pale and nervous.
    c. makes sure there is an armed guard in the room.
    d. usually tells your parents you are not living up to your potential.

8. What style of music does your family enjoy?

a. Classical or folk
b. Rock or pop
c. Gregorian chanting monks
d. Moans from the dungeons

9. When a friend comes over to your house, what happens?

a. Your granny gives him a nice, shiny apple.
b. All the family photographs start gossiping among themselves.
c. Your sister tries to give him a makeover.
d. You play video games.

10. Where is your family's favourite vacation spot?

a. Vegas, baby!
b. A campsite.
c. The "cottage" — it's so "peaceful" and "quiet" there.
d. Disneyland.

SCORING

1. a1 b2 c4 d3
2. a4 b1 c2 d3
3. a1 b3 c2 d4
4. a2 b1 c3 d4
5. a1 b4 c2 d3
6. a4 b1 c2 d3
7. a1 b3 c4 d2
8. a2 b1 c3 d4
9. a2 b4 c3 d1
10. a3 b1 c4 d2

YOUR FAMILY'S WEIRDNESS LEVEL . . .

10–12 Normal. In fact your family's so normal, that actually makes them kinda weird!

13–22 Odd ducks. So the neighbours think you are a tad peculiar. Big deal — they have a stuffed moose nailed to the roof of their car.

23–32 Total strange-rs. You're right — other people do give you funny looks when you go to the mall. Keep a low profile, and consider moving to Sasquatch country to be with more of your kind.

33–40 Ultra-weird. You always wanted to be special, didn't you? Well now you know the truth — you are. Your clan sends the weird-meter into the red zone. Don't worry, though, the X-Men are mutants too, and they're superheroes!

HOW BAD IS YOUR BREATH?

1. You worship . . .
a. cheese.
b. garlic and onions.
c. garlic, onions, salami and mouldering cheese.

2. How often do you brush your teeth?
a. Two to three times a month.
b. Two to three times a day, just like the dentist recommends.
c. You mean people brush their teeth?

3. Your parents . . .
a. call you "our son, the stinkbomb."
b. make sure you brush at least twice a day.
c. have run away from home without leaving a forwarding address.

4. You have been invited . . .
a. to join a special military unit as their secret weapon.
b. to be a poster boy for the Canadian Dental Association for your perfect smile.
c. to be a poster boy for the Canadian Dental Association for your perfectly awful dental hygiene.

5. You used to sleep with a teddy bear named Binkster, but . . .
a. his face turned black.
b. he ran away from home with your parents.
c. he had an unfortunate accident in the washing machine.

6. Have you ever received any of the following gifts?
a. A year's supply of mouthwash.
b. A free toothbrush from the dentist.
c. A ticket to a far away country.

7. What is your favourite breakfast dish?
a. Pickled herring in cream sauce.
b. Cereal or toast.
c. Blue cheese and garlic omelette.

8. Do you wear braces?
a. No, please see question 4, response b.
b. Yes.
c. No, because the wires keep disintegrating.

SCORING

1. a1 b2 c3
2. a3 b1 c5
3. a3 b1 c5
4. a6 b1 c5
5. a3 b5 c1
6. a3 b1 c5
7. a3 b1 c5
8. a1 b2 c4

8–12 Pin a rose on your nose! If only flowers could smell as sweet!

13–22 Occasionally wretched. On a bad day your breath can slay a llama from 50 paces. When dogs get a whiff, they howl at the moon. Even swine are impressed by your odiferous orifice.

23–30 Incredibly disgusting. Vomitacious does not begin to describe the aroma of your exhalations, nor the feeling in the pit of the stomach of anyone who comes within sniffing distance. Avoid mouth-breathing in small, enclosed spaces if you wish to reach adulthood.

31–37 Beyond revolting. When you speak, clouds flee from the sky, the oceans roll back from the shore and babies everywhere start to cry. Stinkologists from major universities have attempted to study your uniquely horrible breath, but most have died trying. Reduce global warming and habitat destruction: brush your teeth!

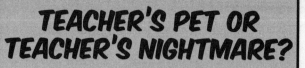
1. When your teacher asks for someone to hand out work to the class, what do you do?
a. Nothing.
b. Raise my hand eagerly — I love to help!
c. Offer to help — I'll get to talk to my friends as I go around the classroom.

2. How often do you forget your school supplies — pencils, notebook, homework, etc.?
a. Occasionally
b. Almost every day
c. Never

3. Do you frequently get in trouble for talking in class?
a. Yes
b. No

4. Do you try your best on all your school work?
a. Absolutely. I like to learn and do well at school.
b. Usually. Sometimes, if the work is hard or boring, I just try and get through it quickly.
c. Why bother? It's all a waste of time anyway.

5. What's your bedtime?
a. I go to bed whenever I want — sometimes late, sometimes early.
b. I always go to bed by nine so I can wake up easily in the morning.
c. Gotta catch the late show — I can sleep in math.

6. There's an argument going on between a few of your classmates. You . . .
a. have nothing to do with it.
b. are right there — in the thick of things, as usual!
c. watch to see if something really exciting happens.

7. When you have trouble with your classwork, you . . .
a. ask the teacher for extra help.
b. crack a joke and wind up getting into trouble.
c. quietly ask the person next to you for help.

8. Your teacher has assigned a book report to the class. She wants you to draw a scene from the book. You hate drawing! What do you do?
a. Nothing, I just pretend I forgot about the assignment and don't do it.
b. Ask the teacher if I can do my report in another way since I don't like to draw.
c. Try it — I'll do my best, even on a project I don't like.

9. You have to do a group project. There are three kids in your group. Which kid are you?
a. The one that gets everybody else organized and does most of the work.
b. The one that does my part — I'll do the research I've been assigned.
c. The one who keeps things light — work doesn't have to be so serious!

10. The teacher has just asked you a question. You don't know the answer. What do you do?
a. Put my head down and mumble that I don't know.
b. Make a big joke out of it.
c. Get angry and act snotty to the teacher.

1. a1 b3 c2
2. a2 b1 c3
3. a0 b5
4. a3 b2 c1
5. a2 b3 c1
6. a3 b0 c1
7. a3 b1 c2
8. a0 b3 c4
9. a3 b2 c0
10. a2 b1 c0

HOW YOU RATE

6–10 Heartbreak hotel. They have your picture in the staff room marked *Hazardous Material — Proceed with Caution!*

11–20 Satisfactory. Teachers have a hard time remembering your name. That's great — it means they won't automatically blame you for breaking stuff.

21+ Teacher's pet. What do teachers love most in the world? Piles of homework, endless math drills and kids just like you.

CAN YOU DECODE ADULT-SPEAK?

Match the grownups' words on the left to what they really mean on the right.

They say . . .

1. Did you brush your hair?
2. Is that what you're wearing to Great Aunt Agnes' house?
3. Supper's ready!
4. Wait till your father gets home!
5. You are grounded for a week!
6. I'll meet you in front of the school as soon as the bell rings.
7. I've tried something healthy for dinner — you're going to love it.
8. Be nice to your little brother.
9. I love you just the way you are.
10. What did you say?
11. How was school today?
12. I'd like to hear your opinion.
13. I'll think about it.
14. Is it okay with you if we stop off at the mall for a few minutes?
15. I'll be with you in two secs!
16. I love your art project! It's so . . . creative!

But they mean . . .

a. No.
b. Unless I get stuck at work/the store, then you'll have to wait.
c. I've tried something new that looks and tastes like sawdust mixed with seaweed.
d. I'm not really paying attention — I'll ask this again.
e. Don't complain when your brother wrecks your stuff.
f. You are in big trouble.
g. We're going to the mall.
h. No TV or computer until I forget I punished you.
i. Good thing you're good at math — you're no da Vinci.
j. Change your clothes right now.
k. Come back later – I'm busy.
l. Not that you have any say, I just think it's nice to ask.
m. I love you just the way you are.
n. Go brush your hair!
o. You're REALLY in big trouble.
p. Come to the dinner table in about 15 minutes.

69

1n, 2j, 3p, 4f, 5h, 6b, 7c, 8e, 9m, 10o, 11d, 12l, 13a, 14g, 15k, 16i

HOW YOU RATE

0–4 Novice decoder. Do you often find yourself confused when speaking with your parents or teachers? Don't worry, you'll figure them out before you're sixteen — then it will be your turn to confuse them!

5–8 Level II decoder. You've got the basics down. Just be patient with grownups, and you'll have them figured out in no time.

9–12 Advanced placement. You have an excellent grasp on adult-speak. You might make it to your teen years without getting grounded.

13–16 Super decoder. You know when no means no and when yes means no. Your grasp of adult-speak is so perfect, it may indicate you have actually crossed over into adulthood. If you have recently told someone to go make their bed, you must immediately go watch back-to-back episodes of SpongeBob SquarePants!

HOW WELL DO YOU UNDERSTAND GIRLS?

1. You have to buy a birthday present for a girl in your class. You choose a . . .
a. horse book.
b. sparkly bracelet.
c. little plastic purse with a stuffed kitty in it.

2. You see two girls sitting together at lunch. They are . . .
a. best friends.
b. fighting.
c. plotting against another girl.

3. A girl in your class has just said, "Hi!" to you. That means . . .
a. she likes you.
b. she hates you.
c. she likes your best friend.

4. Which of these three movies would a girl most like to see?
a. *Transformers 3*
b. *High School Musical 4*
c. *Barbie's latest adventure*

5. When a girl says, " No problem," it means . . .
a. don't worry about it.
b. you are so dead.
c. I have no idea who you are.

6. Girls like boys who . . .
a. are masculine and strong.
b. are kind.
c. like the same stuff they do.

7. A girl asks you to play one-on-one basketball. You should . . .
a. show her how great a player you are, no matter what it takes.
b. let her win.
c. say, "No, let's just talk."

8. There is one cookie left on the plate. You . . .
a. let the girl you are with have it — you were taught to always be polite.
b. take it — girls always complain about getting fat anyway.
c. tell her to go make some more cookies.

SCORING Give yourself 0 points for each A answer. Give yourself 0 points for each B answer. Give yourself 0 points for each C answer.

HOW YOU RATE

0-0 What were you thinking? You are a boy! You will never understand girls. They are inexplicable, confusing creatures. No matter how hard you try, you will never be able to figure out why they think pink ponies are cute or why they giggle or scream like that. Just smile and nod, and try and escape with your dignity intact.

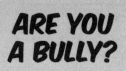

ARE YOU A BULLY?

1. When you get angry, what are you most likely to do?
a. Sulk in my room.
b. Take it out on someone else.
c. Throw a temper tantrum.

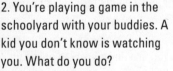

2. You're playing a game in the schoolyard with your buddies. A kid you don't know is watching you. What do you do?
a. Invite him to play.
b. Tell him to get lost.
c. Ignore him.

3. In general, I . . .
a. feel good about myself.
b. wish I could be somebody else.
c. think I'm king of the hill.

4. Have you ever been bullied?
a. No
b. Yes
c. Not sure

5. At home, how are you treated?
a. With respect and affection.
b. I do what I'm told or watch out!
c. Okay, I guess — like a kid.

6. You frequently find your schoolwork . . .
a. neither too easy nor too hard — I can handle it.
b. more challenging than I'd like to admit.
c. it depends on the subject.

7. How do you feel most of the time?
a. Happy, cheerful and optimistic.
b. Sad, angry and irritable.
c. Sometimes happy, sometimes sad — every day is different.

8. You are doing a group project. You tend to . . .
a. divide up the tasks evenly and get to work right away.
b. boss the other kids around.
c. make jokes and fool around.

9. You see some kids picking on a younger boy in the schoolyard. What do you do?
a. Call a teacher over to help.
b. Join in.
c. Stay away.

10. Your friend got a new set of markers that are really cool. You want to trade him your old set for his new set. He doesn't want to. What do you do?
a. It was worth a shot, but no big deal.
b. Pester him and pester him until he gives in.
c. Sweeten the deal by offering him a new pack of gum, too.

SCORING

Give yourself 1 point for each A answer, 3 points for each B answer and 2 points for each C answer.

HOW YOU RATE

10–15. You are gentle and easygoing. You are more likely to stand up to a bully than be one.

16–25. You know bullying is wrong, so maybe you could do a little more to help prevent it. If someone's giving another kid a hard time, instead of joining in or ignoring it, maybe you could try and help out.

26–30. You sometimes take your feelings out on others. Consider talking to a teacher, your parents or another adult you trust about what's going on in your life. They can help you sort out any troubles that are making you feel down.

ARE YOU A GENETIC ODDITY?

Genes are instructions inside your cells for how your body is put together and how it works. Some genes are very common — a lot of people have them. Other genes are rarer — fewer people have them. Do you have any unusual genes? Take this test to find out!

1. Toe Nut
Look at your toes. Which toe is longer, your big toe or your second toe?
a. Second toe
b. Big toe

2. Have Thumb Fun
Hold out your thumb. Can it bend backwards at an angle of 45 degrees or more, or is it straight?
a. Angles at least 45 degrees
b. Straight

3. Hot Dog Bun?
Can you curl your tongue so it resembles a hot dog bun?
a. No
b. Yes

4. That's Ear-ie
Are your earlobes attached to the side of your head, or do they hang free?
a. Attached
b. Hang free

5. Drac Attack
Do you have a "widow's peak" (does your hairline form a point at the front)?
a. No
b. Yes

6. Are you Left Handed?
a. Yes
b. No

7. Eye See!
Do you have brown eyes?
a. No
b. Yes

8. Let's Get this Straight
Is your hair straight, wavy or curly?
a. Curly
b. Wavy or straight

9. Do You Have More Fun?
What colour is your hair?
a. Blond or red
b. Black or brown

Add up the number of A answers. These traits are all less common in the general population than the B answers. The more A answers you have chosen, the rarer a bird you are!

AND THE A'S HAVE IT

1–2 a's Genetically typical. Of the common traits here, you are more than 80% average. So relax — you're not nearly as odd as you feared!

3–5 a's Slightly off kilter. You are pretty average, genetically speaking, but not plain vanilla. A pleasantly refreshing genetic cocktail.

6–7 a's Genetically peculiar. You seem to have a higher percentage than average of atypical genetic traits. This makes you very interesting and unique. Celebrate your quirkiness!

8–9 a's One in a million. You are definitely not ordinary. You are an interesting mixture of traits that make you unique. Enjoy your delightful mixture of rare and extraordinary characteristics.

ARE YOU LEFT BRAINED OR RIGHT BRAINED?

Your brain is divided into halves. Each half is somewhat specialized to do different types of tasks. While we use both sides of our brain to think and function, most people tend to rely on one side of the brain more than the other. We say that side of the brain is "dominant."

Depending on which side of the brain dominates, it can affect your personality, likes and dislikes, and thinking style. Take this quiz to find out which side of your brain is dominant and what that may say about you.

Answer yes or no to each question.

1. I always like to know what time it is.
2. I find following directions can be tricky.
3. It's the simple truth: there is either a right way or a wrong way to do something.
4. I don't like having to stick to a schedule.
5. When I lose something, I picture it in my head to figure out where I last saw it.
6. If I am giving directions, I would rather draw a map than write out the instructions.
7. Doing math is easy for me.
8. I follow my heart more than my head.
9. I always like to read the directions before putting something together.
10. When I'm thinking about the answer to a question, I turn my head to the left.
11. I think I'd make a great detective because I'm good at details.
12. I'm very musical.

13. If someone asks me a question, I usually look up and to the right.
14. When I have to solve a problem, I usually think about similar problems I have solved in the past.
15. If I'm trying to remember a person's name and I can't, I go through the alphabet until I remember it.
16. I believe there is more than one way to look at almost everything.
17. I write with my right hand.
18. I frequently lose track of time.
19. When I climb stairs, I put my right foot on the step first.
20. I wave my hands around a lot when I talk.
21. I really don't like to draw that much.

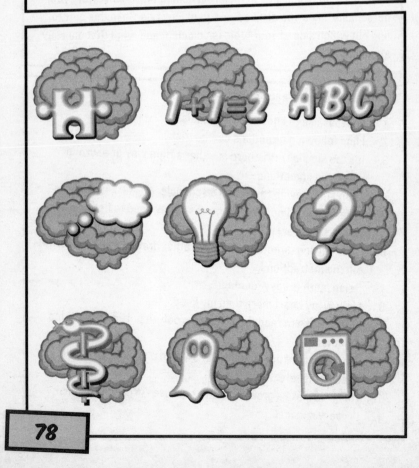

SCORING

Add up the number of YES answers you gave for the ODD numbered questions (1,3,5, etc.): _____
Add up the number of YES answers you gave for the EVEN numbered questions (2,4,6, etc.): _____

If you have more yeses for the odd-numbered questions, it means you are more likely left brained. More yeses for the even-numbered questions means you are likely more right brained.

IF YOU ARE . . .

Left brained:
You are more likely to be logical and detail-oriented, with a preference for facts, facts and more facts. You prefer subjects like math or science that have clear cut, right or wrong answers and rely on order and sequence. You can be very practical, and you are good at coming up with effective strategies for getting the job done.

Right brained:
You are likely very creative. You tend to see the big picture and think all the little details are boring and petty. You love to make up stories, imagine crazy and funny scenes or draw and paint. You rely on your instincts and hunches. You probably have a great sense of humour and can be very entertaining.

ARE YOU A GENIUS?

1. Who is buried in Grant's Tomb?
a. Michael Jackson
b. General Ulysses S. Grant
c. Fred Flintstone

2. Connect the dots.

• •

3. How many corners are there in a three-cornered hat?
a. 3
b. 1
c. 2

4. Which is bigger, the little cat on the left, or the bigger cat on the right?

Little cat   Big cat

5. Can you spell the word "cat?"

6. What shape is this triangle?
a. A triangle
b. A circle
c. A square

7. Can you find your way through the maze?

►START   END

8. What colour is a brown bear?

9. What is your name?

_____

10. Circle the correct number below.

THE CORRECT NUMBER

Optical illusions are images that trick your eyes. Just for fun, look at the images below and see what you can see. Look closely!

Is this an illustration of a triangle?

Is this open book facing toward you or away from you?

Can you count how many legs this elephant has?

Is this top hat taller than it is wide? Use your ruler to see if you're right.

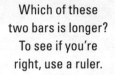

Which of these
two bars is longer?
To see if you're
right, use a ruler.

Is the left end of the
bar darker than the
right end? Fold the
page so the ends are
beside each other.
Were you right?

Do you see dots anywhere
in this illusion? What
happens if you try to focus
on one?

Do you see faces or a cup,
in this picture?

83

USE YOUR EYES — CAN YOU SOLVE THESE?

How good is your spatial sense? Can you figure out puzzles just by looking at them? Find out with this test!

1. Can you divide the large circle into sections by drawing three straight lines? There can only be one labelled circle in each section.

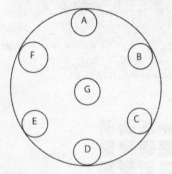

2. In the diagram below, colour in 12 squares so that there are two coloured squares in each horizontal row, each vertical column and along each of the two diagonals.

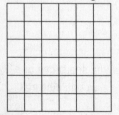

3. Which three shapes can be combined to form a triangle?

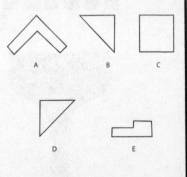

4. Using the image below, can you cross out five lines to leave behind just three original squares?

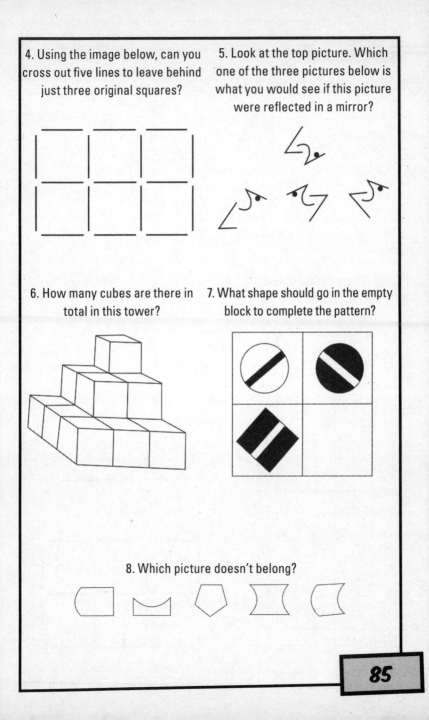

5. Look at the top picture. Which one of the three pictures below is what you would see if this picture were reflected in a mirror?

6. How many cubes are there in total in this tower?

7. What shape should go in the empty block to complete the pattern?

8. Which picture doesn't belong?

1.

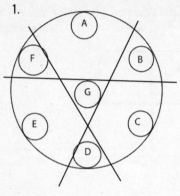

2. There's more than one correct answer. Here are three possible solutions

3. B, C, D

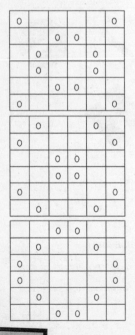

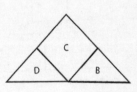

4.

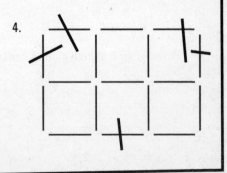

5. The third picture, on the bottom right.

6. 14

7.

8.

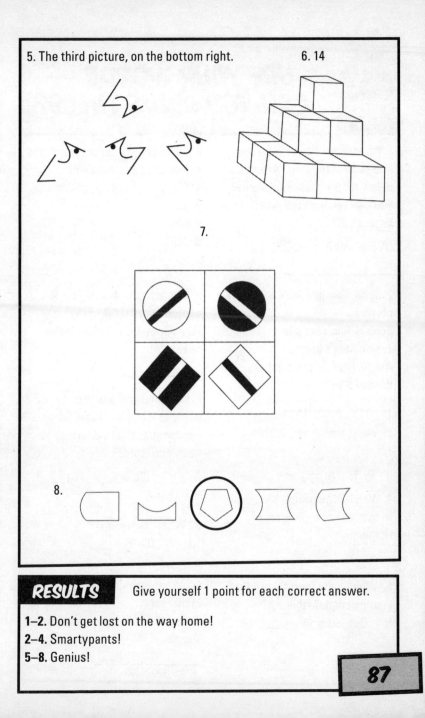

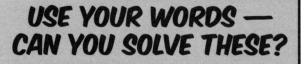

USE YOUR WORDS —
CAN YOU SOLVE THESE?

1. What letter can be inserted into each of the three examples below to turn them into words? You can't change the order of the letters.

DVE   VER   DG

_____

2. John, Tom and Alex are hockey players.
John is Tom's brother.
Tom is Alex's brother.
Alex is NOT John's brother.
Who is Alex?

_____

3. What comes next in this series?

J F M A — —

4. Which is heavier, a kilogram of feathers or a kilogram of titanium?

_____

5. What is the fourth word that would complete this set?
In   Out   Big   _____

6. Complete this sentence: Four is to five as _____ is to eight.
a. Six
b. Seven
c. Nine
d. Ten

7. A bear has built a den for the winter. Three sides of the den face south. What colour is the bear?

_____

8. What four-letter word, if added to the end of these three letter combinations, would turn all of them into words?

Bo____   Cove____   St____

9. What comes next?
10 J Q K ___

10. What word does NOT belong in this set?
Topaz, Ruby, Aquamarine, Garnet, Dazzle

_____

1. O (D**O**VE **O**VER D**O**G)

2. Alex is John's sister.

3. <u>M</u> <u>J</u> (Each letter is the first letter in the names of the months: **J**anuary, **F**ebruary, **M**arch, **A**pril. **M**ay and **J**une come next.)

4. They are exactly the same — they both weigh a kilogram.

5. Small or little

6. b

7. White. For three sides to face south, the den must be at the North Pole. The bear must be a polar bear.

8. RING

9. The answer is A. These are the numbers or symbols on playing cards, in ascending order, beginning with the number 10. The next cards are **J**ack, **Q**ueen, **K**ing and **A**ce.

10. Dazzle. All the other words are names of gemstones.

SCORING

1–2. Clever!
3–5. Practically a genius
6–8. A real brainiac
9–10. Watch out, Einstein!